TADIA'S FAM
IN ROMAN ISCA

JOHN EVANS

Illustrated by Richard Hook

DREF WEN

Isca was a fortress built by the conquering
Roman army to make sure that the Celts of
south Wales obeyed their laws. Tadia lived with
her mother and father outside the walls of Isca.

Her father had once been a soldier, but now he was too old to fight. Her brother, Tadius was still a soldier and he lived inside the fortress, ready to march to any trouble-spot in the Roman Empire.

One day, Tadius brought news to his family that
his century would be leaving Isca soon to fight in
Germany against the enemies of the Romans.
In the final days before he left, Tadia was busy
with her mother, preparing things that her brother
would need for the journey.

While her mother mended the holes in his cloak,
Tadia took out the mortarium to grind the wheat into
flour. She put some in a bag and tied it up, and the
remainder she mixed into dough to make bread,
so that Tadius would have food on his long journey.

5

Meanwhile, in the amphitheatre, Tadius took part
in drill practice, to make sure he was fit
and ready to fight.

His sword and javelin were sharpened.

His armour was polished and then inspected
by Centurion Rufinius.

Like everyone else who lived outside Isca, Tadia
was only allowed into the fortress at certain times
of the day. She enjoyed going to the bath-house
with the other women and children in the
afternoon once her work was finished.

After a quick cold bath, Tadia rubbed oil from her flask into her skin and then lay down, first in the warm room and then in the hot room.

The heat rose from under the floor to make her sweat, before she scraped the dirt and sweat from her body with a strigil.

Then, she returned to the cold bath to cool down,
dried and dressed herself, chatted with her friends
and drank wine.

Back home, as night fell, Tadia lit the oil lamps
and placed bread, cheese and olives on the table,
in readiness for the last meal with Tadius. The
family sat around the table and talked about
the journey ahead. When the meal was finished,
Tadius handed his money-box to his sister.

"Look after this until I return," he said. "If I don't
come back, then use this money to buy the things
you need". With that, he kissed his sister on both
cheeks, and returned to his barracks within the fortress.

Early the following morning, Tadius fastened his lorica, strapped on his helmet and picked up his javelin and shield.

He marched out through the gates of Isca with the
rest of his century and climbed into one of the
waiting ships which were tied up on the river.
Tadia waved tearfully as the ships set sail for
Germany. She wondered what might happen to
Tadius, and if he would return safely …

Time passed. One year, ten years, fifty years.
Tadia and her brother were forgotten. A hundred
years, two hundred years. The Romans left and
Isca began to fall into ruins. The stones were
taken to build new houses.

Weeds covered the courtyard in front of the
bath-house. Five hundred years passed. The roofs
fell in and the buildings collapsed. A thousand
years went by. Earth covered the rubble. Only the
strong stone towers and fortress walls could be seen.

In the middle of the ninteenth century, the fortress of Isca was almost forgotten and a new town, named Caerleon had taken its place. People sometimes found objects belonging to the Romans in the ground. One day, a farmer ploughing a field found a stone which had some strange carvings on it. He called in the archaeologists. They carefully brushed away the soil and, carved into the stone, they found words in Latin, the language of the Romans. Translated into English it said:

"To the spirits of the departed. Tadia Vallaunius lived 65 years and Tadius Exuperatus, her son, lived 37 years having died on the German expedition. Tadia Exuperata the devoted daughter set this up to her mother and brother, beside her father's tomb".

INDEX